# MR WHITE AND THE RAVENS

*Best Wishes*

*Geoff Palmer*

ISBN: 90-76953-27-9

2nd print, August 2001

Copies can be ordered via the Internet: www.gopherpublishers.com
or from
Gopher Publishers UK
14 Harrow Inn Close
Elgin
IV30 1BP
Tel. +44 (0) 1343 550 245
Fax. +44 (0) 1343 550 781

# Mr White and T[...]

by

## Geoff Palmer

### With Illustrations by Jeremy Neville

Gopher Publishers, www.gopherpublishers.com

# Dedication

Dedicated to Henry Larmond, my mother's great grandfather. He had one name, which was Henry. So he took the name of his owner, which was Lamond. And it was written Larmond.

# Foreword

Our behaviour as human beings essentially reflects our ideology and geography; in short, we do as others do, not what we ought to do. Most of what we do or profess has been pre-packaged by our culture. In general, we tend to pre-judge rather than to think for ourselves. Prejudice saves time and keeps us in line with our "own kind". Surely this gang mentality cannot be the essence of our humanity?

To illustrate this, three small incidents come to mind.

I was in a shop a short time ago. Two little boys followed me around the shop for a while. The younger then said, pointing: "Look, there's a Nigger." The older boy then slapped him on the head and said: "It's rude to point…"

Children take their prejudices into adulthood.

Some time ago, I was kept waiting in the reception area of a large institution for an unexpectedly long time. My host then told me, with some embarrassment, that when he rang the receptionist to enquire if I had arrived, he was told by the receptionist that, "Professor Palmer has not arrived, there is just some black guy wanting to see you."

The third incident took place after representing Britain abroad at a conference. As I approached my car, a man jumped out in front of me shouting: "Go back to your country, Nigger." This got out of hand and the police arrived. When asked by the police why he wanted to attack me, the man stuttered: "For Christ sake … you should be on *my* side." I drove home with the thought: "The tutored ignorance of the child has grown into the witting or unwitting evil of the man."

The expression of prejudice comes in many forms. Some people carry out their prejudices with the "sword", others with a "word" or a conspiratorial wink and a nod, overtly or covertly, in public or in institutions.

Notwithstanding, I am optimistic about the capacity of human beings to do good, yet it continues to baffle me what drives people to despise and harm other people because of small genetic differences which are embodied in their creation. Indeed, it seems to escape the small minds of racist fanatics that if different "races" can accept each other's hearts and blood groups, surely they can accept each other's skin colour …

This denial of common humanity must be the ultimate evil or sin for which there should perhaps be no forgiveness or redemption. Yet without forgiveness and redemption there can be no justice and without justice we will never have a community that is peaceful, equitable and successful, where worth is seen primarily as the mitigation of other peoples' suffering. The causes of suffering are various but one cause that is totally unacceptable is when "good" people choose to deny the existence of prejudice which they have never experienced and endured.

**G H Palmer**

# Mr White and The Ravens

*Ignorance and prejudice are the parents of nasty people whose monstrous behaviour we tolerate too often because of indifference, self-interest or shared beliefs. Nastiness, like racism, should be a crime, but then most of us would be criminals.........*

The back door opened and the west winds blew the songs of the birds into the house. Stuart White stood in his doorway. He was a large man of regular habits. Years in the army had made him that way. The water-coloured sun rose slowly and crept along the top of the hill. It was seven in the morning and Stuart White was in his usual place.

The sun glowed, lit behind the trees, turning the trunks deep black but shafts of light passing between the trees set the garden aglow turning a dull collection of shrubs, weeds and uneven lawn into an impressionist masterpiece. The shrubs and weeds grew out of a bed of ill-nourished sandy soil at the top of the garden. The lawn sloped towards the door and was greener at the bottom half than at the top half because the nutrients had drained down with the rain.

Stuart White was proud of his land. "This is my land..." he would say in conversation with us, his neighbours. "I fought the war for my garden and it goes down to the centre of the earth." He had fought the war for many things such as not having to use the metric system, not having to walk on zebra crossings and not having to eat organic food. He had built his garden fence and wall to keep out 'intruders'. It wasn't clear who these intruders were but the marking out of 'his land' was more of a warning than an impregnable obstacle. Stuart White was a solitary man; no one visited except some birds that flew over his 'boundaries' every morning to be fed by him.

The usual mixed gang of birds was on the back wall of the garden waiting for the first piece of food to be thrown onto the lawn. The gang included a flock of aggressive starlings with sharp long beaks, small sparrows of no particular distinction, hyperactive

robins with breasts more rust-brown than red, streetwise wagtails smartly dressed in black and white and a sea-shy seagull which had the loosest of bowel control. Nothing was 'safe' under its flight. There were also two silky feathered ravens of nervous disposition. They sat by themselves on a roof and looked sideways down at Stuart White. They kept their hoarse, distinct croak to a minimum as if not wanting to attract attention. The marmalade cat was asleep at the base of the wall, in full view of the birds. It purred like the engine of a new car. The grey squirrel had not yet arrived. He usually came late. The sandstone wall, with its orange-brown watermarked brushstrokes, sparkled in the rising sun.

To feed the birds was an important part of Stuart White's duty to his country. They were his country's birds. He fed them because they were loyal *Brits* and did not migrate to foreign parts expecting to be adored when they returned. "The country could have sunk while they were lying about in the sun in foreign lands," he often protested to us in the pub. Stuart White believed that birds that migrated were ungrateful and espoused that ingratitude was the worst of sins. He stirred the pot he was holding with his right hand. It contained: wet stale bread mixed with pieces of mouldy cheese, dry stale cake, pieces of boiled potato and decayed bananas mixed with pieces of bacon rind and gristle that had defied his false teeth. He threw a handful of his feed onto the lawn with a sowing action.

The aggressive starlings were the first to land on the lawn and immediately began to stab at the food and at each other. Then came the sparrows, which darted between the starlings and ate with intelligent frenzy. The robins flew forwards and backwards to the wall eating very little, while the wagtail waited until the lawn was empty, flew down quickly, collected small pieces of food and departed gracefully. The cat awoke suddenly. He was about to go through his usual chatter of aggression to impress his master but the birds disappeared so he ran over the lawn and down the side of the house to escape attention. He was afraid of the starlings. More food landed on the lawn. Suddenly the seagull descended on its flat feet and like a giant hoover sucked up three or four pieces of food, climbed steeply into the sky and vanished. The lawn was empty except for the occasional starling and sparrow.

The squirrel appeared. It ran along the wall, stopped at the centre of the lawn and began to eat a piece of

cake. The ravens glided onto the wall with ease and precision. They remained silent but reacted to the slightest noise or movement. Their life seemed to be one of always being ready to fly away to safety. The squirrel knew its place and was confident. The ravens followed the activities of the squirrel. It sat up on its back legs, pulling off pieces of cake with its small paws and putting them into its mouth. It then broke off a succession of large pieces of cake and buried them in the garden bed under a small willow tree. It probably never returned to retrieve the buried bounty. The squirrel was self-possessed, mean and selfish. Stuart White thought this showed character.

It was getting cold. Stuart White was not affected by the cold. His feet were bare and had an unpleasant network of blue veins. He never wore slippers or a dressing gown when he came to the back door. This had been the talking point of many of the women. "It's a disgrace that a grown man should stand in his pyjamas in public view," they would mutter over their fences. This disapproval had no effect on Stuart White because he often said: "Me and my kind have fought and killed foreigners to keep our women from being despoiled and what thanks do they show? They still send food parcels to foreigners and want their own way." He had fought the war so that he could be any way he liked, in his own house.

The longstanding and bitter disapproval of the women began on the day he drove his partner out of the house. We did not know her name. She had been very house-proud, cleaning and washing from early morning to late at night. She had complained bitterly that he did nothing to help her. Then one day she disappeared... The cat had brought a dead mouse into the house. Stuart White hid it under his 'colonial' bag in the corner of the spare room.

One day when she was cleaning with what Stuart White regarded as 'my vacuum sucker', she lifted the bag and found the carcass of the decaying mouse and fainted. After pouring water on her face to revive her, he told her that he had put the mouse under the bag to check that she was cleaning the house properly. She left the house and never returned. Like many unpleasant people he believed that house ownership and past service to country, no matter how questionable, conferred the right to be unreasonable and unjust. Stuart White had no comprehension of a single human race that included women and foreigners.

The squirrel disappeared over the wall. The cat returned to the lawn and sniffed the pieces of food that remained. Stuart White withdrew and closed the door. It was seven thirty and time to get ready for work. The ravens croaked and flapped their wings in a drunken dance. The cat ran through the cat flap, demanding to be fed. He was a coward. His main purpose in life was to start fights with other cats smaller than he was. It was this unpleasant nature that prompted him to pick a

fight with the squirrel. He wailed at the squirrel and sprung on its back. The squirrel turned quickly and bit off a piece of the cat's ear and disappeared over the wall.

The cat was incensed by this defeat. That night he went up the road where the rabbits played, caught one, ate the head and brought the body home. He never ate the bodies of his prey. Maybe it was a form of self-preservation; heads were less likely to be diseased than bodies. He was a killer that spent his life being fed. This appealed to Stuart White. To him, killing was a consequence of survival in conflict. Stuart White once asserted in the pub: "There is no civilisation that has dominated that has not had to do a lot of killing. So, don't knock the 'means' that gave you your 'ends'. Someone had to do it to give you what you have. One day you may have to do it yourself or get someone to do it for you so you can sit in this pub and talk rubbish, laddie."

The sun peeped between the hills and the clouds as the ravens landed softly on the wall and waited. They knew they were not welcome. Stuart White could see them through his bedroom window and shouted: "Clear off, you vermin. Go and eat dead meat off the roads, that's your job. Get out of my garden, you don't belong here, go back to where you've come from – a good lynching, that's what you need." He cursed and rattled the window frame. The ravens took a few skips sideways along the wall and flew back to the roof. They had been feeding in Stuart White's garden for some time, usually when he was out at work or occupied in the house. Stuart White hated rooks and ravens. Their resilience against adversity made him nervous and sapped his energy. He couldn't distinguish one from the other but it didn't matter, he hated them both.

"They are vermin, they eat dead meat," he would lecture, "plus they carry germs, there are too many of them and they make a damn awful noise." And, with a measured degree of menace, he added: "It is the civic duty of decent people like me to send them back to their trees." This cultural catalogue of hate was always followed by the usual lament that he had fought a bloody war to keep out things like that from his home and his country. His wish was that they would migrate and not return. He did not accept that all birds had the same heritage and shared the same creation.

Stuart White's hateful ideology forced the ravens to feed by stealth. They were afraid but determined. They would land on the wall, wait, and when safe, jump

down onto the garden bed. Satisfied that there was no danger, they would hop to the nearest piece of food, pick up mouthfuls in their beaks and fly powerfully over the rooftops, exposing their distinct wedged tails, and disappear into the trees. Though terrified, the ravens had a will to live that transcended the evil of their tormentor and the unfair advantage of their main competitor, the arrogant seagull, who not only had bad manners, but was by nature and nurture, greedy and selfish.

In the face of such unjust competition, the ravens, out of sheer desperation, sometimes attacked the seagull, but the seagull took little notice of them because it knew that its place in the garden of Stuart White was secure. In an unjust world the ravens needed their determination, simply to survive.

Stuart White thought of killing the ravens but he didn't have a 'real' gun and killing with an air gun was not a 'real killing'.

"Killing is ultimate power," he would boast, "only soldiers and the State can do it right. To stop a life, even that of a flea, means that you have stopped, not only the goings on of millions upon millions of years, but you have prevented its future...that is power, laddie. I had it in the war and I used it more than once." As usual, he regarded the stony silence of his audience as indicating 'kith and kin' approval.

He knew the ravens fed from his garden when he was at work during the week so, at the weekends, he hounded them mercilessly, shouting obscenities and chasing them with sticks and stones. He considered it a mistake of creation that ravens could fly so gracefully and that they had survived despite all the hatred that he knew 'most people' had for them. He believed that things that are difficult to destroy have hidden agendas that will be used against him. He was afraid of the ravens. They seemed strange. They didn't relate with other birds. They were things he didn't understand and he believed that nothing good has been said or written about them.

He knew that a few were kept at the Tower of London, but believed this was 'proof' that they symbolised evil and deserved to be hounded from the face of the earth. He developed an urgency with regard to the removal of the ravens. He wrote many letters to the authorities. He got many replies but none that suited him. Running through them was the view that it was up to him to find a way to get rid of the ravens. But, buried in this suggestion was the characteristic ambiguity: eliminate the intruders but don't get caught on a technicality because there were no laws against ravens or rooks living out their natural lives. "There should be," roared Stuart White, "those office people don't have to put up with the constant noise, the filth, and the theft of these useless incomers."

He wasn't satisfied so he called the police. The response to the 999 call was swift, as one would expect if a good citizen were to be in distress because, unpleasant, noisy, singing, black-coloured birds had invaded his property. The police examined the point of intrusion and enquired of the number and description of the intruders before being told that the intruders were *birds* ... ravens or rooks! The police left in disappointment and anger. "It may not matter to you but it matters to me," he shouted as the police drove away in their white Crimestoppers' van. These failures to gain the support of his 'kith and kin' angered him and drove him to find another way of dealing with the ravens.

Like many discoveries, Stuart White's humiliation of the ravens came by accident. Evil acts, though not always intended, usually come from what already exists. It was a weekend and it snowed unexpectedly. There were no tyre marks in the snow on the road. It was early and quiet. The birds sat on the high folds of the roofs because the top of the garden wall was covered with snow, too soft and too deep to walk on. The bright early morning sun had melted the snow from the high folds of the roofs. Gathered there were the starlings, the wagtails, the sparrows, the robins and some finches. The ravens were on a rooftop of their own and the seagull flew over them in large circles.

Stuart White, dressed in his pyjamas, stood in bare feet at his back doorway and threw out his pieces of leftovers onto the snow that was melting on the lawn. They sank immediately. The gang of birds on the roof lifted off together and landed on the snow-covered lawn. The eating activity was frenzied. Soon there was nothing left. They had taken a particular liking for a peeled, rotten banana. They ate it before the stale bread and potatoes. There was no food for the ravens. In desperation for a share, they flew onto the snow-covered wall. The squirrel did not come that morning. It was too cold. Stuart White shouted at the ravens but they flew over the wall and landed defiantly in the snow that covered the lawn. They somehow knew that the snow was a deterrent to a man with bare feet. Nature's laws, like any good law, are difficult to defy.

Stuart White knew that his gang of birds was still hungry so he threw out the leftovers of some spaghetti he had cooked a few days before. The tangled twines of spaghetti landed on the lawn and sank into the snow. The birds descended again and pecked away at the spaghetti until satisfied. The seagull did not bother to descend. From its place in the sky it regarded spaghetti as foreign and unacceptable and flew away, making a raucous scream which hinted that it would rather follow a local boat and eat scraps than eat spaghetti. It ate protein, not carbohydrate … and that was that.

Stuart White retreated to watch the scene from behind the curtains of his bedroom window. The ravens hopped in the soft snow and started to fill their beaks. Every time they did so the slippery spaghetti slipped from their beaks. Stuart White began to laugh. The ravens became desperate; they seemed to need the food. They tried and tried but failed. This provided great amusement for Stuart White and gave him ideas of how to deal with the intruders. The ordeal of the ravens was an accident, but Stuart White lied that he had designed it, "To show them that I am better and smarter than they are." Maybe someone should have objected when he told us this miserable tale in the pub, but we drank our drinks instead.

It was a bad day for the ravens, nevertheless they returned the next day when the sun had melted the dirty white snow and dried the spaghetti. Swift and determined, they gathered up large beak-fulls of the tacky cream-coloured worms of spaghetti and, after repeated trips, cleared the lawn. Despite their ordeal, they came day after day as usual. They grew more relaxed. The weather had improved. The sun shone almost every day and the purple, white and yellow crocuses emerged from the ground together. The croaking of the ravens became more noticeable: three long croaks instead of two, or three and two croaks combined to form a tune, not pretty, but distinct.

This particular Sunday morning was quiet as usual. The low clouds were pink and grey. The birds were up early. Their complex chorus of mixed songs was warming. The familiar quick wind that caused the branches of the trees to grow to one side was warmer but, as usual, it swirled between the houses and made the windows shake. Everything was 'usual' in this village because change was imperceptible. Stuart White was up early too. He wiped the condensation from the glass of his bedroom window and the bright light of the sun shone through the broken clouds lighting the room and created a colloidal haze of dust.

The two ravens were on the wall. As he started to shout the usual abuse, a third raven landed unsteadily between the two ravens. It was smaller than the other two, fluffy and a lighter shade of black. Stuart White

was silent. He hesitated and then asked, in a whisper, "Who are you, bright bird?" The young bird fluttered unsteadily onto the lawn and began to pick up crumbs and eat them. Stuart White hurried to the back door, squinted against the blinding glare of the sun, and threw out pieces of fresh bread to the young bird. It fluttered about, finding and eating them before its parents flew down and led it away into the safety of the tall trees, to teach it the ways of life because for some, continuity of life is the only hope of a fairer future.

Stuart White stood motionless, staring at them. Running through his mind was the thought that "any creature that has fought so hard to protect a life, cannot be as bad as everybody makes out."

The little bird was lucky ... but then, the life of the disadvantaged should never have to depend mainly on luck or on the whims of others.

## Epilogue

Injustice feeds on prejudice and prejudice is that wicked lie through which people distort the truth … it is also a dreadful disease caught in childhood that fosters hate, damages compassions and distorts the mind. Rules can control actions but they do not control minds – prejudice and counter-prejudice solve nothing. Surely, true redemption from prejudice does not come from rules, it comes from education or a sudden moral shock that changes human beings for the better.

# The Author

G. H. PALMER, also known as Geoff Palmer, is a distinguished research Professor of grain science and technology. His teaching, research and consulting interests have been recognised world-wide in universities, and in the malting, brewing and distilling industries and he was pleased to receive the 4th ASBC research award from the USA in 1999 … he was the 'first European' to be given this honour.

Professor Palmer was born in Jamaica. He emigrated from Jamaica to London when he was a boy and initially attended a secondary modern school for 'educationally limited' children, leaving at 15 years of age. During that time he played cricket for London and contends that this small sporting activity was the turning point in the development of his educational fortunes. Subsequently, he worked as a junior laboratory assistant and kitchen attendant before going to university. Since then he has gained BSc, PhD, and DSc degrees and is now a Fellow of various scientific societies. As a result of his innovative research, he was invited to Japan as Visiting Professor and produced the book, 'Cereal Science and Technology' in 1989. He attributes his success to 'luck against the odds, family and friends and the £86 which his mother paid to have him transported from Jamaica to London in 1955'.

Professor Palmer works in Edinburgh. He has spent a considerable amount of time over the last forty years engaged in community work in race relations and with refugees. He believes in equal rights for only one race – the human race.

# The Artist

JEREMY NEVILLE is a talented young artist and illustrator. He was born in Somerset, England. He studied in Edinburgh and Harrow and worked in education. Mr Neville has travelled extensively and has lived and worked in the USA. He has a deep interest in Jamaican culture and music and has spent a considerable amount of time promoting Reggae music in Scotland.

Jeremy Neville lives in Edinburgh and states that these drawings reflect fruitful collaboration with the author and his commitment to race relations.

Layout:        Stephen Young
Font:          Adobe Garamond (14pt)